Mum had some good news.
"Gran is going to meet the Queen,"
she said.

1

A car drew up. It was Gran.
"I am going to meet the Queen," she said.

"Good for you," said Mum.
"What great news."

"I will need to choose a new dress …
and a hat … and new shoes," said Gran.

Gran got a new dress. She had a new hat and new blue shoes.

The time flew by. At last, Mum took Gran to London. Biff, Chip and Kipper went too.

"The Queen lives here," said Gran.

Oh no! The heel on Gran's new, blue shoe came off.

Gran was upset.
"I can't meet the Queen with no heel on
my shoe," she said.

"I can lend you some blue boots,"
said a lady.

"I can glue the heel on," said a man.
"I have a tube of glue in my van."

A big car drew up. A flag flew
on the roof.

13

Chip ran up to the car.
"Stop that boy," called a man.

"Excuse me. Will you help us?"
called Chip.

The car stopped and a man got out.
It was the Duke.

"The heel has come off Gran's new blue shoe," said Chip.

She can't meet the Queen.

"I'll see what I can do," said the Duke.
"Wait by this gate."

Later, a man came to the gate.
He had a box. It was full of blue shoes.

"You can choose from these shoes,"
he said.

Gran went to meet the Queen.
"I do like your shoes," said the Queen.

22

"Gran's blue shoes will be big news," said Biff.